Punctuation

Key Stage 2
For ages 10-11

Practise & Learn

Published by CGP

Editors:
Holly Poynton
Jennifer Underwood
Luke von Kotze

With thanks to Janet Berkeley and
Heather Gregson for the proofreading.

ISBN: 978 1 84762 146 7

Groovy website: www.cgpbooks.co.uk
Printed by Elanders Ltd, Newcastle upon Tyne
Jolly bits of clipart from CorelDRAW®

Psst... photocopying this Workbook isn't allowed, even if you've got a CLA licence. Luckily, it's dead
cheap, easy and quick to order more copies from CGP — just call us on 0870 750 1242. Phew!
Text, design, layout and original illustrations © Coordination Group Publications Ltd. (CGP) 2013
All rights reserved.

Contents

Capital Letters

Start each sentence with a capital letter.

> **T**he hamster fell off his wheel. **H**e landed in his food bowl.

Start proper nouns (names of particular people, places or things) with capital letters.

> When **S**uri went to **W**iltshire, she visited **S**tonehenge.

Rewrite these sentences with capital letters in the correct places.

1 the weather was awful, so jo stayed in.

....

2 lily went to paris for christmas.

....

3 my grandma lives on moon crescent.

....

4 kell bought a puppy and called it bernard.

....

Read this story and circle any word that should start with a capital.

last year my sister faria and i went on holiday to scotland. we stayed by loch ness. on sunday morning i was sitting outside when suddenly i saw a flash of green by the water! i screamed that i could see the monster, and faria raced out to look. i felt very silly when she pointed out that it was just old mr pitt chasing a tent that had blown away.

Full Stops

Sentences often finish with a full stop.

> I fell off my bike yesterday. I don't think anyone noticed.

Where you put full stops can change the meaning of what you write.

> Jamie went to bed at 9. The next morning he woke up.

> Jamie went to bed. At 9 the next morning he woke up.

Add the full stops and underline the letters that should be capitals in the story below. There are five missing full stops and three missing capital letters.

Helen was bored it was the half-term holiday but it had rained solidly all week she had read all her books and played all her games Helen leaned her head against the window and groaned if it carried on like this she might have to resort to doing her homework

Rewrite each pair of sentences. Put the full stop in a different place to change their meaning. Don't forget to use a capital letter at the beginning of each sentence.

1 Carlos got sweets on his birthday. He ate them all.

....

2 Samia sat down. Under the table her cat played quietly.

....

3 Dad sang in the shed. Mum did a jigsaw.

....

Exclamation Marks

You can sometimes finish your sentences with an exclamation mark.

Use an exclamation mark to show that something was said loudly.   ⟹   "Get up!" shouted Ted.

You can also use exclamation marks to show that something makes you angry, frightened or surprised.   ⟹   He was an undercover spy!

Write sentences using the words in the bubbles and an exclamation mark.

brother broken	⟹	....
hair mess	⟹	....
sandwich ghost	⟹	....

Finish the sentences with either a full stop or an exclamation mark.

1 I saw a horrible, slimy monster in the attic ....

2 February is the shortest month of the year ....

3 We went bowling after we went to the cinema ....

4 Her brother owns a talking dog ....

5 The chlorine made her hair turn green ....

6

Some commands end with an exclamation mark. → **Don't move!**

Not all commands need exclamation marks though. Only use one if a command is showing a strong emotion or urgency.

Take a seat. ← You don't need an exclamation mark here.

Tick the commands that are likely to end with an exclamation mark.

1. Tidy your pens away ☐
2. Be quiet immediately ☐
3. Bring a sleeping bag ☐
4. Don't touch that ☐
5. Stop it now ☐
6. Put your shoes here ☐

Complete each sentence so that it needs an exclamation mark.

1. Don't .... !

2. Quick, Kai, ... !

3. I can't believe .... !

4. " ....!" she roared.

Read the passage below and add in four exclamation marks and seven full stops where they're needed.

"Jack, there's a package here for you " shouted Jack's mum from the bottom of the stairs Jack leapt up from his desk excitedly and ran noisily down the stairs, shouting, "I never get packages "

The package was waiting for him on the kitchen table He examined the stamps closely

"It's come all the way from Timbuktu " he said with shock Intrigued, he picked up the box and gave it a quick shake

"Don't do that " said Jack's mum "It's got 'fragile' written on it "

Question Marks

Every direct question should end with a question mark.

| What did she say? | Who ate all the ice cream? |

Questions often start with question words. Here are some of the most common ones.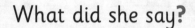

when   where   why   how   who   what

Finish the sentences below with either a question mark or a full stop.

1. What time is it

2. Are you going to school

3. Wait for me here

4. There you are

5. How much is it

6. Why is it so heavy

Write a question word in each gap to complete each question.

1. .... many pizzas have you ordered?

2. .... has been invited to the party?

3. .... did you put the tickets?

Write down a question for each pair of words from the bubble.

egg stolen

plate waffle

shiny turtle

....

....

....

Sentence Practice

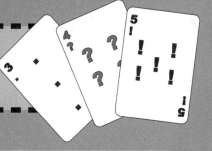

Remember that you can use a full stop, a question mark or an exclamation mark to end a sentence.

Match each sentence with its most likely final punctuation.

Be quiet

Why did you stop

Fred likes chocolate

That's amazing

Where did he go

I'm so excited

Write the most likely final punctuation in each box.

1. Is there any homework ☐

2. Thank you for the drink ☐

3. Please post the letter ☐

4. I hate Science ☐

5. Where is the library ☐

6. Stop right there ☐

Add full stops, question marks and exclamation marks to this passage.

"How many more balloons do we need to blow up " asked Connor
"I think this is the last one," said Mohammed
Suddenly, the boys heard a loud " Pop " Then they heard another and another They looked on in horror as Connor's cat burst their balloons with her sharp claws
"Stop her, Connor " shouted Mohammed

Commas

Commas are used to separate items in a list.

> I need to buy apples, milk, bread and a sombrero.

You don't need a comma between the last item and the word 'and'.

You can also use a comma with a connective (joining words like 'so', 'but', 'and') to link sentences together.

The comma goes before the connective.

> I went to the park. It rained.

> I went to the park, **but** it rained.

Add commas in the correct places in the sentences below.

1. My favourite months are April May October and August.

2. The train stops at York Leeds Huddersfield and Manchester.

3. I've never tasted aubergine courgette or radish.

4. You will need some glitter a glue stick and a sheet of paper.

Add commas in the correct places and underline the connectives.

1. I want to buy a snake so I've been saving up for months.

2. Betsy is away this week so someone needs to clear her desk.

3. I was going to bake Drew a cake but I forgot to buy flour.

4. We lost our umbrellas at the theatre and then it started to rain.

5. Heather went to the zoo but she was scared of the emus.

Commas can also separate extra information in a sentence.

My dog, who is called Billy, is 5 years old today.

Rewrite the sentences below adding the extra information in the box. Use commas where they are needed.

1 The school play was really funny.

which raised lots of money

....

2 Fatima plays hockey for our county.

who is older than me

....

3 My teacher has three pet lobsters.

a strange man

....

4 China is in Asia.

which is my favourite country

....

Read the passage below and put commas in the correct places.

June Ramsbottom the cleverest girl in school won the school's spelling competition. In the first round she managed to spell xylophone barracuda mozzarella and tambourine. Mr Jones who is our head teacher struggled to pronounce a couple of the words in the second round but June still managed to spell them correctly. June is going to Birmingham to compete in the national competition next month. I hope her winning streak continues but I wonder if she remembers that it was me who told her how to spell 'biology' in Year Four!

Colons

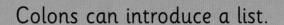

Colons can introduce a list.

> Gus only eats three things: cakes, burgers and carrots.

You can also use a colon if you want to add some information to explain your sentence. *The part before the colon must make sense on its own.*

> We were delighted: no more pea soup!

Add a colon to each of the sentences below.

1 I still need to buy supplies plasters, a poncho and a haggis.

2 We saw lots of creatures butterflies, moths and two spiders.

3 My dog is in disgrace my homework has been chewed again.

Tick the sentences below which use colons correctly.

1 There were peanuts in two rooms: the bedroom and the kitchen. ☐

2 Be careful on the roads: ice has made them slippery. ☐

3 I play lots of sports at school football: tennis and hockey. ☐

Write a sentence below using a colon correctly.

....

....

Semi-colons

Semi-colons separate longer phrases in a list, usually when there are already commas in some of the phrases.

> Flo wears a red top, which she hates, on Wednesdays; a green denim skirt on Thursdays; and a black bowler hat on Fridays.

Semi-colons can also join two sentences together. Both sentences must be about the same thing and make sense on their own.

> The milk looked a bit funny; we threw it out.

The semi-colon often replaces words like 'so' or 'and'.

Finish the sentence using the words from the box and semi-colons.

> clowns who sing and play the guitar   spiders with seven legs
> cauliflower cheese, the lumpy kind   and dinosaurs in bow ties

Gerry is afraid of ....

....

....

Add a semi-colon to each of the sentences below.

1 Lesley plays the harmonica she doesn't play the banjo.

2 It's Claude's birthday let's buy him something nice.

3 The butcher weighed the chops he liked to be precise.

4 Jon and Sam wear capes they often trip over them.

Splitting Sentences

It can be tricky to know when to use commas, colons and semi-colons. These pages will give you plenty of practice to help you remember.

Add commas in the correct places in the sentences below.

1. The kitchen flooded so we cooked dinner in the living room.

2. Toby Amir Selena Justin and Nicky are invited.

3. The school disco was brilliant but I got tired towards the end.

4. I'm not allowed to eat crisps but I don't really mind.

Add semi-colons in the correct places in the sentences below.

1. I helped Mum with the painting she said I did a good job.

2. It's half-term next week I'm going camel riding in Turkey.

3. Doug is too short to sit there he can't reach the table.

4. I tried to write a book it wasn't very good.

Add colons in the correct places in the sentences below.

1. Noah only likes two types of fruit strawberries and kiwis.

2. There was only one thing we could blame for the smell the dog.

3. I looked excitedly at my watch two hours until home time.

4. Claudia always forgets the same thing her toothbrush.

Add commas, colons and semi-colons in the boxes below.

1 My brother ☐ who is called Nigel ☐ is obsessed with snakes.

2 I love zombie movies ☐ Jim prefers vampire movies.

3 I own three birds ☐ a parrot ☐ a budgie and a pelican.

4 We tried to go to the zoo ☐ but the rhino had escaped.

5 The frame was priceless ☐ the painting was worth nothing.

6 I didn't win first prize ☐ but I'm glad I was able to take part.

7 My dad only taught me one thing ☐ how to wrestle a bear.

8 My mum's cooking my favourite meal ☐ sausage, beans and chips.

Copy out the passage below, adding semi-colons and colons.

During the summer holidays I went to Greece with my family Mum, Dad, me and my little sister, Maggie. We did loads of exciting things we went swimming in the sea, which was really clear and blue we went to a tiny restaurant, where I ate some tasty squid and we also got to go to an amazing water park. I hope we can go back soon!

....

....

....

....

....

....

Apostrophes

Apostrophes can be used to show where letters have been missed out of a word. These are called apostrophes of omission.

do not ➡ don't   will not ➡ won't   I had ➡ I'd

Words like these are called contractions.

Sometimes the letters in a contraction don't quite match the words it's made from.

Draw lines to match each contraction with its longer version.

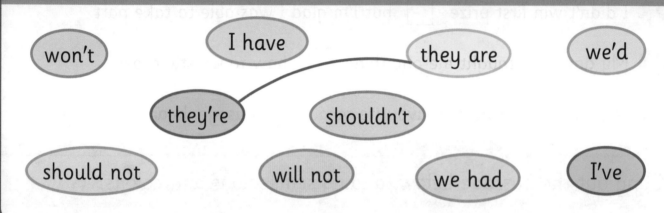

won't   I have   they are   we'd

they're   shouldn't

should not   will not   we had   I've

Circle all the contractions in the passage. Write each contraction on the lines below and write out its full version.

We're going on a boat trip tomorrow. I don't really want to go because I'm afraid there might be sharks in the water, but I've got to go otherwise I'll have to spend the whole day sat in the hotel with Uncle Billy. He's not going because he wants to watch the cricket in the hotel lobby.

1   we're   we are   4   ....

2   5   ....

3   6   ....

Practise and Learn

Punctuation

Ages 10-11

Answers

This section shows each of the pages from the book with the answers filled out.

The pages are laid out in the same way as the book itself, so the questions can be easily marked by you, or by your child.

There are also helpful learning tips with some of the pages.

4

Capital Letters

Start each sentence with a capital letter.

> The hamster fell off his wheel. He landed in his food bowl.

Start proper nouns (names of particular people, places or things) with capital letters.

> When Suri went to Wiltshire, she visited Stonehenge.

Rewrite these sentences with capital letters in the correct places.

1. the weather was awful, so jo stayed in.
   The weather was awful, so Jo stayed in.

2. lily went to paris for christmas.
   Lily went to Paris for Christmas.

3. my grandma lives on moon crescent.
   My grandma lives on Moon Crescent.

4. kell bought a puppy and called it bernard.
   Kell bought a puppy and called it Bernard.

Read this story and circle any word that should start with a capital.

(Last) year my sister (Maria) and (I) went on holiday to (scotland.) we stayed by (loch) (ness.) (on) (sunday) morning (I) was sitting outside when suddenly (I) saw a flash of green by the water! (I) screamed that (I) could see the monster, and (Maria) raced out to look. (I) felt very silly when she pointed out that it was just old (mr) (pitt) chasing a tent that had blown away.

4

5

Full Stops

Sentences often finish with a full stop.

> I fell off my bike yesterday. I don't think anyone noticed.

Where you put full stops can change the meaning of what you write.

> Jamie went to bed at 9. The next morning he woke up.

> Jamie went to bed. At 9 the next morning he woke up.

Add the full stops and underline the letters that should be capitals in the story below. There are five missing full stops and three missing capital letters.

Helen was bored. it was the half-term holiday but it had rained solidly all week. she had read all her books and played all her games. Helen leaned her head against the window and groaned. if it carried on like this she might have to resort to doing her homework.

Rewrite each pair of sentences. Put the full stop in a different place to change their meaning. Don't forget to use a capital letter at the beginning of each sentence.

1. Carlos got sweets on his birthday. He ate them all.
   Carlos got sweets. On his birthday he ate them all.

2. Samia sat down. Under the table her cat played quietly.
   Samia sat down under the table. Her cat played quietly.

3. Dad sang in the shed. Mum did a jigsaw.
   Dad sang. In the shed Mum did a jigsaw.

5

6 — Exclamation Marks

You can sometimes finish your sentences with an exclamation mark.

Use an exclamation mark to show that something was said loudly. → "Get up!" shouted Ted.

You can also use exclamation marks to show that something makes you angry, frightened or surprised. → He was an undercover spy!

Write sentences using the words in the bubbles and an exclamation mark.

VARIOUS ANSWERS POSSIBLE

- brother broken ⇨ My brother has broken the record!
- hair mess ⇨ My hair is such a mess!
- sandwich ghost ⇨ A ghost has eaten my sandwich!

Finish the sentences with either a full stop or an exclamation mark.

1. I saw a horrible, slimy monster in the attic !
2. February is the shortest month of the year .
3. We went bowling after we went to the cinema .
4. Her brother owns a talking dog !
5. The chlorine made her hair turn green !

7

Some commands end with an exclamation mark. → Don't move!
Not all commands need exclamation marks though. Only use one if a command is showing a strong emotion or urgency. → Take a seat. You don't need an exclamation mark here.

Tick the commands that are likely to end with an exclamation mark.

1. Tidy your pens away ☐
2. Be quiet immediately ☑
3. Bring a sleeping bag ☐
4. Don't touch that ☑
5. Stop it now ☑
6. Put your shoes here ☐

Complete each sentence so that VARIOUS ANSWERS POSSIBLE

1. Don't tease the tigers !
2. Quick, Kai, shut the gate before the bull gets out !
3. I can't believe you forgot the eggs !
4. "I'm the champion of the world !" she roared.

Read the passage below and add in four exclamation marks and seven full stops where they're needed.

"Jack, there's a package here for you!" shouted Jack's mum from the bottom of the stairs. Jack leapt up from his desk excitedly and ran noisily down the stairs, shouting, "I never get packages!"
The package was waiting for him on the kitchen table. He examined the stamps closely.
"It's come all the way from Timbuktu!" he said with shock.
Intrigued, he picked up the box and gave it a quick shake.
"Don't do that!" said Jack's mum. "It's got 'fragile' written on it."

8 — Question Marks

Every direct question should end with a question mark.

What did she say? — Who ate all the ice cream?

Questions often start with question words. Here are some of the most common ones. → when where why how who what

Finish the sentences below with either a question mark or a full stop.

1. What time is it ?
2. Are you going to school ?
3. Wait for me here .
4. There you are .
5. How much is it ?
6. Why is it so heavy ?

Write a question word in each gap to complete each question.

1. How many pizzas have you ordered?
2. Who has been invited to the party?
3. Where did you put the tickets?

Write down a question for each pair of words from the bubble.

- egg stolen — When did the egg get stolen?
- plate waffle — Where is the plate for this waffle?
- shiny turtle — How did the turtle get so shiny?

VARIOUS ANSWERS POSSIBLE

9 — Sentence Practice

Remember that you can use a full stop, a question mark or an exclamation mark to end a sentence.

Match each sentence with its most likely final punctuation.

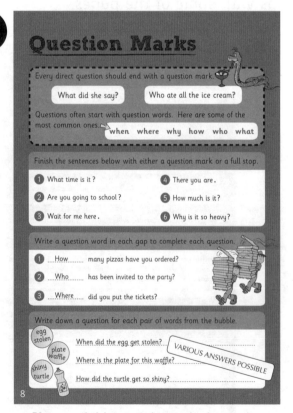

Be quiet — Why did you stop — Fred likes chocolate — That's amazing
Where did he go — I'm so excited
! ?

Write the most likely final punctuation in each box.

1. Is there any homework [?]
2. Thank you for the drink [.]
3. Please post the letter [.]
4. I hate Science [!]
5. Where is the library [?]
6. Stop right there [!]

Add full stops, question marks and exclamation marks to this passage.

"How many more balloons do we need to blow up?" asked Connor.
"I think this is the last one," said Mohammed.
Suddenly, the boys heard a loud "Pop!" Then they heard another and another. They looked on in horror as Connor's cat burst their balloons with her sharp claws!
"Stop her, Connor!" shouted Mohammed.

If your child struggles with this page, get them to copy out and learn the most common question words.

Commas

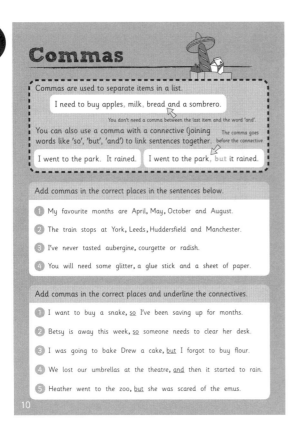

Commas are used to separate items in a list.

> I need to buy apples, milk, bread and a sombrero.

You don't need a comma between the last item and the word 'and'.

You can also use a comma with a connective (joining words like 'so', 'but', 'and') to link sentences together. *The comma goes before the connective.*

> I went to the park. It rained. I went to the park, but it rained.

Add commas in the correct places in the sentences below.

1. My favourite months are April, May, October and August.

2. The train stops at York, Leeds, Huddersfield and Manchester.

3. I've never tasted aubergine, courgette or radish.

4. You will need some glitter, a glue stick and a sheet of paper.

Add commas in the correct places and underline the connectives.

1. I want to buy a snake, <u>so</u> I've been saving up for months.

2. Betsy is away this week, <u>so</u> someone needs to clear her desk.

3. I was going to bake Drew a cake, <u>but</u> I forgot to buy flour.

4. We lost our umbrellas at the theatre, <u>and</u> then it started to rain.

5. Heather went to the zoo, <u>but</u> she was scared of the emus.

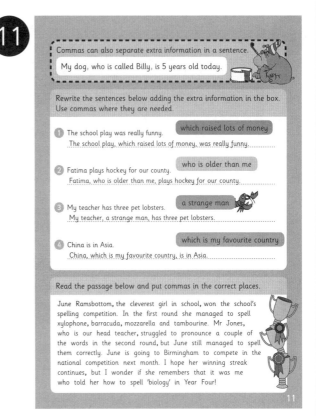

Commas can also separate extra information in a sentence.

> My dog, who is called Billy, is 5 years old today.

Rewrite the sentences below adding the extra information in the box. Use commas where they are needed.

1. The school play was really funny.   *which raised lots of money*
   The school play, which raised lots of money, was really funny.

2. Fatima plays hockey for our county.   *who is older than me*
   Fatima, who is older than me, plays hockey for our county.

3. My teacher has three pet lobsters.   *a strange man*
   My teacher, a strange man, has three pet lobsters.

4. China is in Asia.   *which is my favourite country*
   China, which is my favourite country, is in Asia.

Read the passage below and put commas in the correct places.

June Ramsbottom, the cleverest girl in school, won the school's spelling competition. In the first round she managed to spell xylophone, barracuda, mozzarella and tambourine. Mr Jones, who is our head teacher, struggled to pronounce a couple of the words in the second round, but June still managed to spell them correctly. June is going to Birmingham to compete in the national competition next month. I hope her winning streak continues, but I wonder if she remembers that it was me who told her how to spell 'biology' in Year Four!

Colons

Colons can introduce a list.

> Gus only eats three things: cakes, burgers and carrots.

You can also use a colon if you want to add some information to explain your sentence. *The part before the colon must make sense on its own.*

> We were delighted: no more pea soup!

Add a colon to each of the sentences below.

1. I still need to buy supplies: plasters, a poncho and a haggis.

2. We saw lots of creatures: butterflies, moths and two spiders.

3. My dog is in disgrace: my homework has been chewed again.

Tick the sentences below which use colons correctly.

1. There were peanuts in two rooms: the bedroom and the kitchen. ✓

2. Be careful on the roads: ice has made them slippery. ✓

3. I play lots of sports at school football: tennis and hockey. ☐

Write a sentence below using a colon correctly.

I took only one thing with me: my lucky hat.   *VARIOUS ANSWERS POSSIBLE*

Semi-colons

Semi-colons separate longer phrases in a list, usually when there are already commas in some of the phrases.

> Flo wears a red top, which she hates, on Wednesdays; a green denim skirt on Thursdays; and a black bowler hat on Fridays.

Semi-colons can also join two sentences together. Both sentences must be about the same thing and make sense on their own.

> The milk looked a bit funny; we threw it out.

The semi-colon often replaces words like 'so' or 'and'.

Finish the sentence using the words from the box and semi-colons.

> clowns who sing and play the guitar   spiders with seven legs
> cauliflower cheese, the lumpy kind   and dinosaurs in bow ties

Gerry is afraid of clowns who sing and play the guitar; spiders with seven legs; cauliflower cheese, the lumpy kind; and dinosaurs in bow ties.

Add a semi-colon to each of the sentences below.

1. Lesley plays the harmonica; she doesn't play the banjo.

2. It's Claude's birthday; let's buy him something nice.

3. The butcher weighed the chops; he liked to be precise.

4. Jon and Sam wear capes; they often trip over them.

Ask your child to check that the words before the colon work as a sentence on their own and then that the words after the colon add details or an explanation.

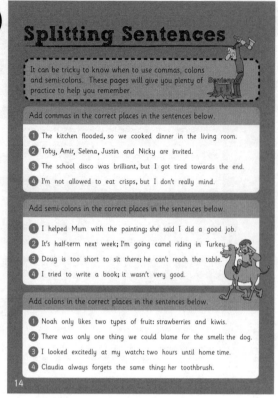

14 — Splitting Sentences

It can be tricky to know when to use commas, colons and semi-colons. These pages will give you plenty of practice to help you remember.

Add commas in the correct places in the sentences below.

1. The kitchen flooded, so we cooked dinner in the living room.
2. Toby, Amir, Selena, Justin and Nicky are invited.
3. The school disco was brilliant, but I got tired towards the end.
4. I'm not allowed to eat crisps, but I don't really mind.

Add semi-colons in the correct places in the sentences below.

1. I helped Mum with the painting; she said I did a good job.
2. It's half-term next week; I'm going camel riding in Turkey.
3. Doug is too short to sit there; he can't reach the table.
4. I tried to write a book; it wasn't very good.

Add colons in the correct places in the sentences below.

1. Noah only likes two types of fruit: strawberries and kiwis.
2. There was only one thing we could blame for the smell: the dog.
3. I looked excitedly at my watch: two hours until home time.
4. Claudia always forgets the same thing: her toothbrush.

14

15

Add commas, colons and semi-colons in the boxes below.

1. My brother [,] who is called Nigel [,] is obsessed with snakes.
2. I love zombie movies [;] Jim prefers vampire movies.
3. I own three birds [:] a parrot [,] a budgie and a pelican.
4. We tried to go to the zoo [,] but the rhino had escaped.
5. The frame was priceless [;] the painting was worth nothing.
6. I didn't win first prize [,] but I'm glad I was able to take part.
7. My dad only taught me one thing [:] how to wrestle a bear.
8. My mum's cooking my favourite meal [:] sausage, beans and chips.

Copy out the passage below, adding semi-colons and colons.

During the summer holidays I went to Greece with my family Mum, Dad, me and my little sister, Maggie. We did loads of exciting things we went swimming in the sea, which was really clear and blue we went to a tiny restaurant, where I ate some tasty squid and we also got to go to an amazing water park. I hope we can go back soon!

During the summer holidays I went to Greece with my family:
Mum, Dad, me and my little sister, Maggie. We did loads of
exciting things: we went swimming in the sea, which was really
clear and blue; we went to a tiny restaurant, where I ate some
tasty squid; and we also got to go to an amazing water park.
I hope we can go back soon!

15

If your child finds these pages tricky,
go over the pages on commas,
semi-colons and colons with them,
to make sure they understand.

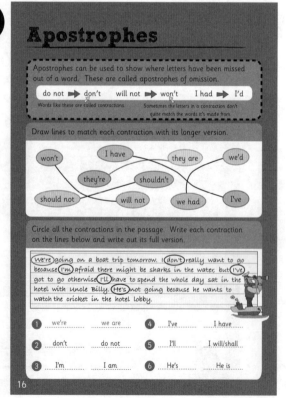

16 — Apostrophes

Apostrophes can be used to show where letters have been missed out of a word. These are called apostrophes of omission.

do not ➡ don't   will not ➡ won't   I had ➡ I'd

Words like these are called contractions.   Sometimes the letters in a contraction don't quite match the words it's made from.

Draw lines to match each contraction with its longer version.

won't   I have   they are   we'd
they're   shouldn't
should not   will not   we had   I've

Circle all the contractions in the passage. Write each contraction on the lines below and write out its full version.

(We're) going on a boat trip tomorrow. I (don't) really want to go because (I'm) afraid there might be sharks in the water, but (I've) got to go otherwise (I'll) have to spend the whole day sat in the hotel with Uncle Billy. (He's) not going because he wants to watch the cricket in the hotel lobby.

1. we're — we are
2. don't — do not
3. I'm — I am
4. I've — I have
5. I'll — I will/shall
6. He's — He is

16

17

Write the full versions of the contractions below.

1. we've ➡ we have
2. shouldn't ➡ should not
3. you're ➡ you are
4. could've ➡ could have
5. weren't ➡ were not
6. isn't ➡ is not

Tick the sentences which use apostrophes correctly.

1. He couldv'e been a professional footballer. ☐
2. Darcy wasn't happy with the portion sizes. ☑
3. "Don't think you can fool me," warned Mr Vicktor. ☑
4. The pool's booked for a party on Tuesday. ☑

Rewrite each sentence below. Change the bold words into the correct contractions.

1. I **did not** have enough money, so I **could not** buy a magazine.
   I didn't have enough money, so I couldn't buy a magazine.

2. He **had** been watching TV when he **should have** been revising.
   He'd been watching TV when he should've been revising.

3. Salman **cannot** come to my party because **he is** visiting his grandma.
   Salman can't come to my party because he's visiting his grandma.

4. **They will** show you the beach tomorrow if **there is** time.
   They'll show you the beach tomorrow if there's time.

17

Possessive Apostrophes

Possessive apostrophes show that something belongs to someone.

Beryl's stamps ⟹ The stamps belonging to Beryl.

You don't need an apostrophe to show that the word is plural.

Apostrophe Mail

Tick the phrases which use apostrophes correctly.

1. Pedro's apple's ☐
2. Gloria's business ☑
3. The children's school ☑
4. The wizards wand's ☐
5. The babys' spoon ☐
6. The dragon's treasure ☑

Rewrite the phrases below using an apostrophe.

1. The squid belonging to Martha — Martha's squid
2. The carrot belonging to Danika — Danika's carrot
3. The jars belonging to Mrs Penny — Mrs Penny's jars
4. The boots belonging to the firemen — The firemen's boots

Write a sentence using a possessive apostrophe and the words below.

Nana Elsie rocking chair

Auntie Annie was doing her knitting in Nana Elsie's rocking chair.

VARIOUS ANSWERS POSSIBLE

If a word is **singular** and ends with an 's', add an apostrophe and an 's' on the end. ⟹ Mr Jones's crow

The crows' corn ⟸ If a word is **plural** and ends with an 's', just put an apostrophe on the end.

Look at the apostrophe and say whether the word is singular or plural. Write 'P' if you think it's plural, and 'S' if you think it's singular.

1. The boys' secret den [P]
2. George's spider [S]
3. Carlos's rocket [S]
4. The roads' pavement [P]
5. The vampire's goblet [S]
6. James's magic bean [S]

Underline all the possessive apostrophes in the passage below.

Dear Fraser,
I'm having a brilliant time staying at Aunty Zhang's house in China. Today we went to Beijing to the Forbidden City — it's huge, and it used to be the Emperor's palace! Tonight we had uncle Hu's famous sweet and sour pork for dinner — it was just as good as he promised it would be.

Tomorrow we are going to see the city's botanical gardens — we are going to take the next door neighbour's dog for a walk and have a picnic somewhere. Apparently all the trees' leaves are starting to turn orange — uncle Hu says Beijing looks beautiful in autumn.

Love from, Gemma
xx

Rewrite the following phrases using an apostrophe.

1. The pens belonging to the authors — The authors' pens
2. The feathers belonging to the swans — The swans' feathers
3. The cookies belonging to Agnes — Agnes's cookies

Its and It's

The word 'its' without an apostrophe means 'belonging to it'.

The bird flew back to its nest. ⟸ The nest belongs to the bird.

The word 'it's' with an apostrophe is a contraction of either 'it is' or 'it has'.

It's kind of you to visit. ⟸ Here 'it's' means 'it is'.

It's been a great holiday. ⟸ Here 'it's' means 'it has'.

Tick the phrases which use 'its' and 'it's' correctly.

1. It's only fair that you go in goal. ☑
2. The cat licked it's tail miserably. ☐
3. Its been cancelled because of the rain. ☐
4. Its foundations were damaged in the earthquake. ☑

Complete the sentences below with 'it's' or 'its'.

1. It's 20 miles to Leeds from here.
2. The horse nibbled its saddle.
3. He told me it's been hit by a meteor.
4. It's taken me 3 months to save up this money.
5. The town was proud of its magnificent statue.
6. The parrot flapped its wings.

Say whether 'it's' is a contraction of 'it is' or 'it has'.

1. What have you done to my room? It's a mess! — It is
2. It's been a rather boring afternoon. — It has
3. It's taken Karim all week to finish his homework. — It has
4. Where's my purse? I think it's been stolen! — It has
5. The weatherman said it's going to rain today. — It is

Write a sentence using the correct form of 'it's' and 'its'.

it's (it is) → It's going to be sunny all day.

it's (it has) → It's been ages since the circus came to our town.

its → The lizard has eaten its dinner.

VARIOUS ANSWERS POSSIBLE

Add apostrophes (where needed) to the sentences below.

1. I can't believe it's Saturday already.
2. Where's my budgie? I think it's flown away!
3. The dog buried its bone in a deep hole.
4. It's eaten all the grain in my shed.
5. The goat awoke from its delightful dream.

To help your child with these pages, get them to practise reading <u>it's</u> out loud as <u>it is</u>.

22

Speech Marks

Speech marks, also called **inverted commas**, go around the words someone actually says. Speech marks always come in pairs.

The porter asked, "Can I help you with your bags?"

Speech usually starts with a capital letter — even if it starts halfway through a sentence.

The speech marks go after the final piece of punctuation.

Tick the sentences which use speech marks correctly.

1. "Where did the orangutan go"? asked Gertie. ☐
2. Funda whispered, "There's someone in the house." ☑
3. How many custard pies do we need?" ☐
4. "I love learning about speech marks!" said Pete. ☑

Put speech marks around the speech below.

1. "Fi ! Fie ! Fo ! Fum !" bellowed the giant .
2. "Let's go to the cinema ," said Dennis .
3. Ava beamed with happiness , "Thanks for the presents ! "
4. "I bet they're going to France ," Lucy whispered to herself .
5. "Where have you put your coat ?" asked Poppy .
6. "Take your shoes off please ," instructed Uncle Khalid .
7. "Over here !" shouted Jacob . "Over here !"

22

23

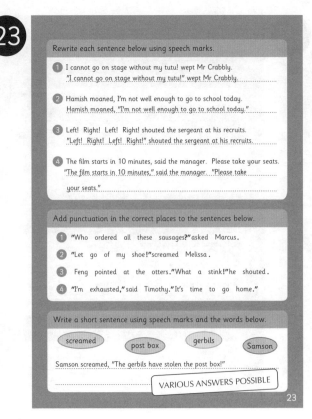

Rewrite each sentence below using speech marks.

1. I cannot go on stage without my tutu! wept Mr Crabbly.
   "I cannot go on stage without my tutu!" wept Mr Crabbly.
2. Hamish moaned, I'm not well enough to go to school today.
   Hamish moaned, "I'm not well enough to go to school today."
3. Left! Right! Left! Right! shouted the sergeant at his recruits.
   "Left! Right! Left! Right!" shouted the sergeant at his recruits.
4. The film starts in 10 minutes, said the manager. Please take your seats.
   "The film starts in 10 minutes," said the manager. "Please take your seats."

Add punctuation in the correct places to the sentences below.

1. "Who ordered all these sausages?" asked Marcus .
2. "Let go of my shoe!" screamed Melissa .
3. Feng pointed at the otters. "What a stink!" he shouted .
4. "I'm exhausted," said Timothy. "It's time to go home."

Write a short sentence using speech marks and the words below.

(screamed) (post box) (gerbils) (Samson)

Samson screamed, "The gerbils have stolen the post box!"

VARIOUS ANSWERS POSSIBLE

23

24

Direct and Reported Speech

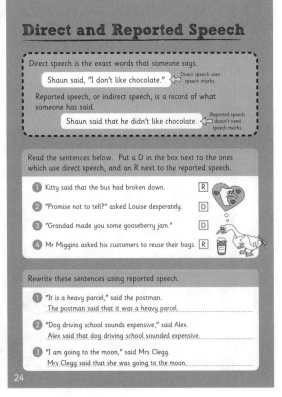

Direct speech is the exact words that someone says.

Shaun said, "I don't like chocolate." ← Direct speech uses speech marks.

Reported speech, or indirect speech, is a record of what someone has said.

Shaun said that he didn't like chocolate. ← Reported speech doesn't need speech marks.

Read the sentences below. Put a D in the box next to the ones which use direct speech, and an R next to the reported speech.

1. Kitty said that the bus had broken down. [R]
2. "Promise not to tell?" asked Louise desperately. [D]
3. "Grandad made you some gooseberry jam." [D]
4. Mr Miggins asked his customers to reuse their bags. [R]

Rewrite these sentences using reported speech.

1. "It is a heavy parcel," said the postman.
   The postman said that it was a heavy parcel.
2. "Dog driving school sounds expensive," said Alex.
   Alex said that dog driving school sounded expensive.
3. "I am going to the moon," said Mrs Clegg.
   Mrs Clegg said that she was going to the moon.

24

25

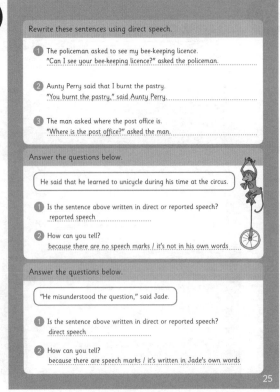

Rewrite these sentences using direct speech.

1. The policeman asked to see my bee-keeping licence.
   "Can I see your bee-keeping licence?" asked the policeman.
2. Aunty Perry said that I burnt the pastry.
   "You burnt the pastry," said Aunty Perry.
3. The man asked where the post office is.
   "Where is the post office?" asked the man.

Answer the questions below.

He said that he learned to unicycle during his time at the circus.

1. Is the sentence above written in direct or reported speech?
   reported speech
2. How can you tell?
   because there are no speech marks / it's not in his own words

Answer the questions below.

"He misunderstood the question," said Jade.

1. Is the sentence above written in direct or reported speech?
   direct speech
2. How can you tell?
   because there are speech marks / it's written in Jade's own words

25

For more practice, get your child to point out direct and reported speech in their favourite story books.

Hyphens

Hyphens are used to show which word an adjective describes.

a new-car salesman

This shows that the word 'new' describes the word 'car'. This means that the salesman sells new cars.

a new car-salesman

This shows that the word 'new' describes the words 'car-salesman'. This means that the salesman is new.

Hyphens are used to join words together or add a prefix. Some words are written with hyphens so they aren't confused with similar words.

I re-covered the chair.

I've recovered from my cold.

're-covered' means 'to cover again'. It needs a hyphen to show that it means something different from 'recovered' which means 'to find' or 'get better'.

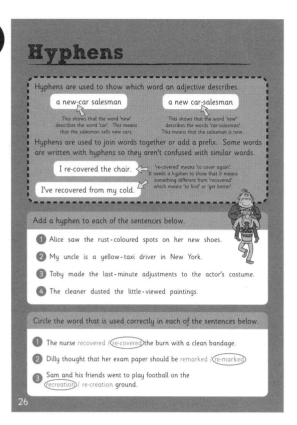

Add a hyphen to each of the sentences below.

1. Alice saw the rust-coloured spots on her new shoes.
2. My uncle is a yellow-taxi driver in New York.
3. Toby made the last-minute adjustments to the actor's costume.
4. The cleaner dusted the little-viewed paintings.

Circle the word that is used correctly in each of the sentences below.

1. The nurse recovered / (re-covered) the burn with a clean bandage.
2. Dilly thought that her exam paper should be remarked / (re-marked)
3. Sam and his friends went to play football on the (recreation) / re-creation ground.

Dashes

Use dashes to separate extra information in a sentence.

My friend — if you can call her that — dyed my hair orange.

If the extra information is in the **middle** of the sentence, use **two** dashes.

Noah brought a ferret to school — an amazing pet!

If the extra information is at the **end** of the sentence, use only **one** dash.

Add a dash to each of the sentences below.

1. The skate park is closing – it's such a shame.
2. We queued up to meet the wrestler – it was worth it.
3. He was too short to press the button – I did it for him.
4. It's lamb chops for dinner – they are my favourite.

Rewrite these sentences using a pair of dashes.

a crazy, smelly spaniel   my dog Taco   likes to play fetch.

My dog Taco — a crazy, smelly spaniel — likes to play fetch.

fell down that winter.   the treehouse   the one Dad built

The tree house — the one Dad built — fell down that winter.

Brackets

Brackets separate off part of a sentence that is less important than the rest.

The Great Stupendo (York's best magician) is my cousin.

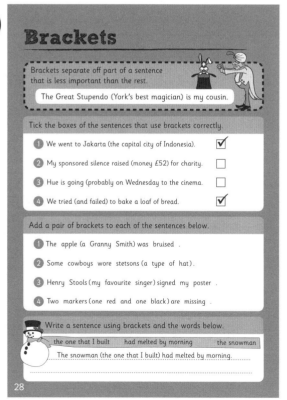

Tick the boxes of the sentences that use brackets correctly.

1. We went to Jakarta (the capital city of Indonesia). ✓
2. My sponsored silence raised (money £52) for charity. ☐
3. Hue is going (probably on Wednesday to the cinema. ☐
4. We tried (and failed) to bake a loaf of bread. ✓

Add a pair of brackets to each of the sentences below.

1. The apple (a Granny Smith) was bruised .
2. Some cowboys wore stetsons (a type of hat) .
3. Henry Stools (my favourite singer) signed my poster .
4. Two markers (one red and one black) are missing .

Write a sentence using brackets and the words below.

the one that I built   had melted by morning   the snowman

The snowman (the one that I built) had melted by morning.

Writing Lists

You can write a list to summarise information.

Use bullet points or numbered lists to organise your points.
- Bullet points are useful for general lists.
- Numbered lists are for points that need to go in an order, like instructions.

Read the text below. Summarise the main points in a list.

Hello Gary,
While I'm away on the coach trip would you mind feeding my dog? Oh, and whilst you're in the flat, you might as well water my plants. If you could pop out and buy some milk and bread, that would be wonderful. Could you turn the heating off too?
Thanks dearie, love Nana xx
P.S. The oven hasn't been cleaned in a while...

Things to do for Nana
- Feed dog
- Water plants
- Buy milk and bread
- Turn heating off
- Clean oven

Write B next to the lists where you think you should use bullet points. Write N where a numbered list would be better.

1. a list of steps in a recipe — N
2. a shopping list — B
3. instructions for using a washing machine — N
4. a list of people to invite to a party — B
5. an ordered list of the best-selling books — N
6. directions for walking to school — N

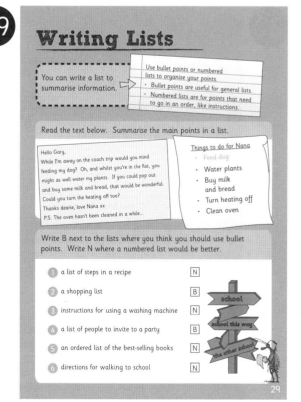

As an extension task, get your child to help you write out a shopping list using bullet points.

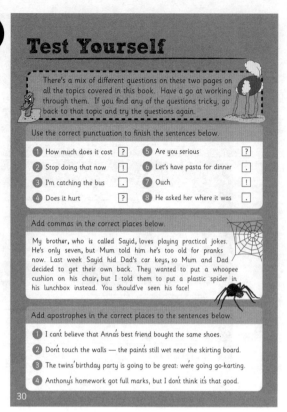

30

Test Yourself

There's a mix of different questions on these two pages on all the topics covered in this book. Have a go at working through them. If you find any of the questions tricky, go back to that topic and try the questions again.

Use the correct punctuation to finish the sentences below.

1. How much does it cost `?`
2. Stop doing that now `!`
3. I'm catching the bus `.`
4. Does it hurt `?`
5. Are you serious `?`
6. Let's have pasta for dinner `.`
7. Ouch `!`
8. He asked her where it was `.`

Add commas in the correct places below.

My brother, who is called Sayid, loves playing practical jokes. He's only seven, but Mum told him he's too old for pranks now. Last week Sayid hid Dad's car keys, so Mum and Dad decided to get their own back. They wanted to put a whoopee cushion on his chair, but I told them to put a plastic spider in his lunchbox instead. You should've seen his face!

Add apostrophes in the correct places to the sentences below.

1. I can't believe that Anna's best friend bought the same shoes.
2. Don't touch the walls — the paint's still wet near the skirting board.
3. The twins' birthday party is going to be great: we're going go-karting.
4. Anthony's homework got full marks, but I don't think it's that good.

30

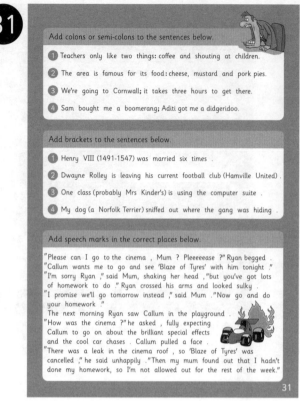

31

Add colons or semi-colons to the sentences below.

1. Teachers only like two things: coffee and shouting at children.
2. The area is famous for its food: cheese, mustard and pork pies.
3. We're going to Cornwall; it takes three hours to get there.
4. Sam bought me a boomerang; Aditi got me a didgeridoo.

Add brackets to the sentences below.

1. Henry VIII (1491-1547) was married six times .
2. Dwayne Rolley is leaving his current football club (Hamville United) .
3. One class (probably Mrs Kinder's) is using the computer suite .
4. My dog (a Norfolk Terrier) sniffed out where the gang was hiding .

Add speech marks in the correct places below.

"Please can I go to the cinema , Mum ? Pleeeeease ?" Ryan begged .
"Callum wants me to go and see 'Blaze of Tyres' with him tonight ."
"I'm sorry Ryan ," said Mum, shaking her head ,"but you've got lots of homework to do ." Ryan crossed his arms and looked sulky .
"I promise we'll go tomorrow instead ," said Mum ."Now go and do your homework ."
The next morning Ryan saw Callum in the playground .
"How was the cinema ?" he asked , fully expecting Callum to go on about the brilliant special effects and the cool car chases . Callum pulled a face .
"There was a leak in the cinema roof , so 'Blaze of Tyres' was cancelled ," he said unhappily ."Then my mum found out that I hadn't done my homework, so I'm not allowed out for the rest of the week."

31

If your child finds the last exercise on this page tricky, they might find it helpful to read it out loud first.

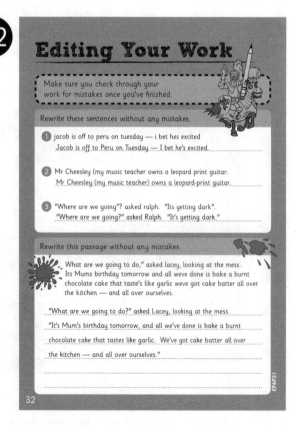

32

Editing Your Work

Make sure you check through your work for mistakes once you've finished.

Rewrite these sentences without any mistakes.

1. jacob is off to peru on tuesday — i bet hes excited
   Jacob is off to Peru on Tuesday — I bet he's excited.

2. Mr Cheesley (my music teacher owns a leopard print guitar.
   Mr Cheesley (my music teacher) owns a leopard-print guitar.

3. "Where are we going"? asked ralph. "Its getting dark".
   "Where are we going?" asked Ralph. "It's getting dark."

Rewrite this passage without any mistakes.

What are we going to do," asked lacey, looking at the mess. Its Mums birthday tomorrow and all weve done is bake a burnt chocolate cake that taste's like garlic weve got cake batter all over the kitchen — and all over ourselves.

"What are we going to do?" asked Lacey, looking at the mess.
"It's Mum's birthday tomorrow, and all we've done is bake a burnt
chocolate cake that tastes like garlic. We've got cake batter all over
the kitchen — and all over ourselves."

32

Write the full versions of the contractions below.

1. we've ⟹ ....
2. shouldn't ⟹ ....
3. you're ⟹ ....
4. could've ⟹ ....
5. weren't ⟹ ....
6. isn't ⟹ ....

Tick the sentences which use apostrophes correctly.

1. He couldv'e been a professional footballer. ☐
2. Darcy wasn't happy with the portion sizes. ☐
3. "Don't think you can fool me," warned Mr Vicktor. ☐
4. The pool's booked for a party on Tuesday. ☐

Rewrite each sentence below. Change the bold words into the correct contractions.

1. I **did not** have enough money, so I **could not** buy a magazine.

....

2. **He had** been watching TV when he **should have** been revising.

....

3. Salman **cannot** come to my party because **he is** visiting his grandma.

....

4. **They will** show you the beach tomorrow if **there is** time.

....

17

Possessive Apostrophes

Possessive apostrophes show that something belongs to someone.

Beryl's stamps ⟹ The stamps belonging to Beryl.

You don't need an apostrophe to show that the word is plural.

Apostrophe Mail

Tick the phrases which use apostrophes correctly.

1. Pedro's apple's ☐
2. Gloria's business ☐
3. The children's school ☐
4. The wizards wand's ☐
5. The babys' spoon ☐
6. The dragon's treasure ☐

Rewrite the phrases below using an apostrophe.

1. The squid belonging to Martha   Martha's squid ....

2. The carrot belonging to Danika   ....

3. The jars belonging to Mrs Penny   ....

4. The boots belonging to the firemen   ....

Write a sentence using a possessive apostrophe and the words below.

Nana Elsie rocking chair

....

....

18

If a word is **singular** and ends with an 's', add an apostrophe and an 's' on the end. ⇒ Mr Jones**'s** crow

The crows**'** corn ⇐ If a word is **plural** and ends with an 's', just put an apostrophe on the end.

Look at the apostrophe and say whether the word is singular or plural. Write 'P' if you think it's plural, and 'S' if you think it's singular.

1 The boys' secret den ☐   4 The roads' pavement ☐

2 George's spider ☐   5 The vampire's goblet ☐

3 Carlos's rocket ☐   6 James's magic bean ☐

Underline all the possessive apostrophes in the passage below.

Dear Fraser,
I'm having a brilliant time staying at Aunty Zhang's house in China. Today we went to Beijing to the Forbidden City — it's huge, and it used to be the Emperor's palace! Tonight we had Uncle Hu's famous sweet and sour pork for dinner — it was just as good as he promised it would be.

Tomorrow we are going to see the city's botanical gardens — we are going to take the next door neighbour's dog for a walk and have a picnic somewhere. Apparently all the trees' leaves are starting to turn orange — Uncle Hu says Beijing looks beautiful in autumn.

Love from, Gemma

xx

Rewrite the following phrases using an apostrophe.

1 The pens belonging to the authors ....

2 The feathers belonging to the swans ....

3 The cookies belonging to Agnes ....

19

Its and It's

The word 'its' without an apostrophe means 'belonging to it'.

The bird flew back to **its** nest. ⟵ The nest belongs to the bird.

The word 'it's' with an apostrophe is a contraction of either 'it is' or 'it has'.

It's kind of you to visit. ⟵ Here 'it's' means 'it is'.

It's been a great holiday. ⟵ Here 'it's' means 'it has'.

Tick the phrases which use 'its' and 'it's' correctly.

1. It's only fair that you go in goal. ☐

2. The cat licked it's tail miserably. ☐

3. Its been cancelled because of the rain. ☐

4. Its foundations were damaged in the earthquake. ☐

Complete the sentences below with 'it's' or 'its'.

1. .... 20 miles to Leeds from here.

2. The horse nibbled .... saddle.

3. He told me .... been hit by a meteor.

4. .... taken me 3 months to save up this money.

5. The town was proud of .... magnificent statue.

6. The parrot flapped .... wings.

Say whether 'it's' is a contraction of 'it is' or 'it has'.

1. What have you done to my room? **It's** a mess! ....

2. **It's** been a rather boring afternoon. ....

3. **It's** taken Karim all week to finish his homework. ....

4. Where's my purse? I think **it's** been stolen! ....

5. The weatherman said **it's** going to rain today. ....

Write a sentence using the correct form of 'it's' and 'its'.

it's (it is) ➔ ....
....

it's (it has) ➔ ....
....

its ➔ ....
....

Add apostrophes (where needed) to the sentences below.

1. I can't believe **it s** Saturday already.

2. Where's my budgie? I think **it s** flown away!

3. The dog buried **it s** bone in a deep hole.

4. **It s** eaten all the grain in my shed.

5. The goat awoke from **it s** delightful dream.

Speech Marks

Speech marks, also called **inverted commas**, go around the words someone actually says. Speech marks always come in pairs.

The porter asked, "Can I help you with your bags?"

Speech usually starts with a capital letter — even if it starts halfway through a sentence.

The speech marks go after the final piece of punctuation.

Tick the sentences which use speech marks correctly.

1. "Where did the orangutan go"? asked Gertie. ☐

2. Funda whispered, "There's someone in the house." ☐

3. How many custard pies do we need?" ☐

4. "I love learning about speech marks!" said Pete. ☐

Put speech marks around the speech below.

1. Fi ! Fie ! Fo ! Fum ! bellowed the giant .

2. Let's go to the cinema , said Dennis .

3. Ava beamed with happiness , Thanks for the presents !

4. I bet they're going to France , Lucy whispered to herself .

5. Where have you put your coat ? asked Poppy .

6. Take your shoes off please , instructed Uncle Khalid .

7. Over here ! shouted Jacob . Over here !

Rewrite each sentence below using speech marks.

1. I cannot go on stage without my tutu! wept Mr Crabbly.

....

2. Hamish moaned, I'm not well enough to go to school today.

....

3. Left! Right! Left! Right! shouted the sergeant at his recruits.

....

4. The film starts in 10 minutes, said the manager. Please take your seats.

....

....

Add punctuation in the correct places to the sentences below.

1. Who ordered all these sausages asked Marcus

2. Let go of my shoe screamed Melissa

3. Feng pointed at the otters What a stink he shouted

4. I'm exhausted said Timothy It's time to go home

Write a short sentence using speech marks and the words below.

screamed   post box   gerbils   Samson

....

....

23

Direct and Reported Speech

Direct speech is the exact words that someone says.

> Shaun said, "I don't like chocolate." ⟵ Direct speech uses speech marks.

Reported speech, or indirect speech, is a record of what someone has said.

> Shaun said that he didn't like chocolate. ⟵ Reported speech doesn't need speech marks.

Read the sentences below. Put a D in the box next to the ones which use direct speech, and an R next to the reported speech.

1 Kitty said that the bus had broken down. ☐

2 "Promise not to tell?" asked Louise desperately. ☐

3 "Grandad made you some gooseberry jam." ☐

4 Mr Miggins asked his customers to reuse their bags. ☐

Rewrite these sentences using reported speech.

1 "It is a heavy parcel," said the postman.

....

2 "Dog driving school sounds expensive," said Alex.

....

3 "I am going to the moon," said Mrs Clegg.

....

Rewrite these sentences using direct speech.

1 The policeman asked to see my bee-keeping licence.

   ....

2 Aunty Perry said that I burnt the pastry.

   ....

3 The man asked where the post office is.

   ....

Answer the questions below.

> He said that he learned to unicycle during his time at the circus.

1 Is the sentence above written in direct or reported speech?

   ....

2 How can you tell?

   ....

Answer the questions below.

> "He misunderstood the question," said Jade.

1 Is the sentence above written in direct or reported speech?

   ....

2 How can you tell?

   ....

Hyphens

Hyphens are used to show which word an adjective describes.

| a new-car salesman | a new car-salesman |

This shows that the word 'new' describes the word 'car'. This means that the salesman sells new cars.

This shows that the word 'new' describes the words 'car-salesman'. This means that the salesman is new.

Hyphens are used to join words together or add a prefix. Some words are written with hyphens so they aren't confused with similar words.

I re-covered the chair.

I've recovered from my cold.

're-covered' means 'to cover again'. It needs a hyphen to show that it means something different from 'recovered' which means 'to find' or 'get better'.

Add a hyphen to each of the sentences below.

1. Alice saw the rust coloured spots on her new shoes.

2. My uncle is a yellow taxi driver in New York.

3. Toby made the last minute adjustments to the actor's costume.

4. The cleaner dusted the little viewed paintings.

Circle the word that is used correctly in each of the sentences below.

1. The nurse recovered / re-covered the burn with a clean bandage.

2. Dilly thought that her exam paper should be remarked / re-marked.

3. Sam and his friends went to play football on the recreation / re-creation ground.

Dashes

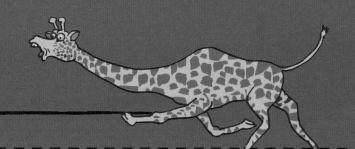

Use dashes to separate extra information in a sentence.

> My friend — if you can call her that — dyed my hair orange.

If the extra information is in the **middle** of the sentence, use **two** dashes.

> Noah brought a ferret to school — an amazing pet!

If the extra information is at the **end** of the sentence, use only **one** dash.

Add a dash to each of the sentences below.

1. The skate park is closing it's such a shame.

2. We queued up to meet the wrestler it was worth it.

3. He was too short to press the button I did it for him.

4. It's lamb chops for dinner they are my favourite.

Rewrite these sentences using a pair of dashes.

> a crazy, smelly spaniel   likes to play fetch.
>   my dog Taco

....

> fell down that winter.   the one Dad built
>   the treehouse

....

27

Brackets

Brackets separate off part of a sentence
that is less important than the rest.

> The Great Stupendo (York's best magician) is my cousin.

Tick the boxes of the sentences that use brackets correctly.

1. We went to Jakarta (the capital city of Indonesia). ☐

2. My sponsored silence raised (money £52) for charity. ☐

3. Hue is going (probably on Wednesday to the cinema. ☐

4. We tried (and failed) to bake a loaf of bread. ☐

Add a pair of brackets to each of the sentences below.

1. The apple a Granny Smith was bruised .

2. Some cowboys wore stetsons a type of hat .

3. Henry Stools my favourite singer signed my poster .

4. Two markers one red and one black are missing .

Write a sentence using brackets and the words below.

| the one that I built | had melted by morning | the snowman |

....

....

Writing Lists

You can write a list to summarise information.

Use bullet points or numbered lists to organise your points.
- Bullet points are useful for general lists.
- Numbered lists are for points that need to go in an order, like instructions.

Read the text below. Summarise the main points in a list.

Hello Gary,

While I'm away on the coach trip would you mind feeding my dog? Oh, and whilst you're in the flat, you might as well water my plants. If you could pop out and buy some milk and bread, that would be wonderful. Could you turn the heating off too?

Thanks dearie, love Nana xx

P.S. The oven hasn't been cleaned in a while...

Things to do for Nana
- Feed dog

Write B next to the lists where you think you should use bullet points. Write N where a numbered list would be better.

1. a list of steps in a recipe ☐

2. a shopping list ☐

3. instructions for using a washing machine ☐

4. a list of people to invite to a party ☐

5. an ordered list of the best-selling books ☐

6. directions for walking to school ☐

Test Yourself

There's a mix of different questions on these two pages on all the topics covered in this book. Have a go at working through them. If you find any of the questions tricky, go back to that topic and try the questions again.

Use the correct punctuation to finish the sentences below.

1 How much does it cost ☐

2 Stop doing that now ☐

3 I'm catching the bus ☐

4 Does it hurt ☐

5 Are you serious ☐

6 Let's have pasta for dinner ☐

7 Ouch ☐

8 He asked her where it was ☐

Add commas in the correct places below.

My brother who is called Sayid loves playing practical jokes. He's only seven but Mum told him he's too old for pranks now. Last week Sayid hid Dad's car keys so Mum and Dad decided to get their own back. They wanted to put a whoopee cushion on his chair but I told them to put a plastic spider in his lunchbox instead. You should've seen his face!

Add apostrophes in the correct places to the sentences below.

1 I cant believe that Annas best friend bought the same shoes.

2 Dont touch the walls — the paints still wet near the skirting board.

3 The twins birthday party is going to be great: were going go-karting.

4 Anthonys homework got full marks, but I dont think its that good.

Add colons or semi-colons to the sentences below.

1 Teachers only like two things coffee and shouting at children.

2 The area is famous for its food cheese, mustard and pork pies.

3 We're going to Cornwall it takes three hours to get there.

4 Sam bought me a boomerang Aditi got me a didgeridoo.

Add brackets to the sentences below.

1 Henry VIII 1491-1547 was married six times .

2 Dwayne Rolley is leaving his current football club Hamville United .

3 One class probably Mrs Kinder's is using the computer suite .

4 My dog a Norfolk Terrier sniffed out where the gang was hiding .

Add speech marks in the correct places below.

Please can I go to the cinema , Mum ? Pleeeeease ? Ryan begged .
Callum wants me to go and see 'Blaze of Tyres' with him tonight .
I'm sorry Ryan , said Mum, shaking her head , but you've got lots
of homework to do . Ryan crossed his arms and looked sulky .
I promise we'll go tomorrow instead , said Mum . Now go and do
your homework .
The next morning Ryan saw Callum in the playground .
How was the cinema ? he asked , fully expecting
Callum to go on about the brilliant special effects
and the cool car chases . Callum pulled a face .
There was a leak in the cinema roof , so 'Blaze of Tyres' was
cancelled , he said unhappily . Then my mum found out that I hadn't
done my homework, so I'm not allowed out for the rest of the week.

Editing Your Work

Make sure you check through your work for mistakes once you've finished.

Rewrite these sentences without any mistakes.

1. jacob is off to peru on tuesday — i bet hes excited

....

2. Mr Cheesley (my music teacher owns a leopard print guitar.

....

3. "Where are we going"? asked ralph. "Its getting dark".

....

Rewrite this passage without any mistakes.

What are we going to do," asked lacey, looking at the mess. Its Mums birthday tomorrow and all weve done is bake a burnt chocolate cake that taste's like garlic weve got cake batter all over the kitchen — and all over ourselves.

....

....

....

....

....

....

FP6P21